DINO-HEROES

ADAPTED BY MEREDITH RUSU

FROM THE SCREENPLAY BY JEREMY ADAMS. STORY BY DAVID SHAYNE.

■SCHOLASTIC

Published in the UK by Scholastic Children's Books, 2020
Euston House, 24 Eversholt Street, London, NW1 1DB
A division of Scholastic Limited

London ~ New York ~ Toronto ~ Sydney ~ Auckland
Mexico City ~ New Delhi ~ Hong Kong

This book was first published in the US by Scholastic Inc.
as three titles:
Owen's Guide to Survival, 2018
Owen's Jurassic Logbook, 2019
Owen to the Rescue, 2019

This edition published in the UK by Scholastic Ltd, 2020
ISBN 978 1407 19880 4

Photo ©: background leaves throughout: Kanea/Shutterstock.

2 4 6 8 10 9 7 5 3 1

Printed in Slovakia

Papers used by Scholastic Children's Books are made from wood
grown in sustainable forests.

www.scholastic.co.uk

TABLE OF CONTENTS

INTRODUCTION

Hey there, second-coolest resident of Jurassic World! I'm the first-coolest, of course. Oh, but I forgot about my dog, Red. He's second-coolest. So, that makes you the third-coolest. Do you accept? Great!

As the newest team member of Jurassic World, I'm sure you're totally stoked to get started on the adventure of a lifetime. Seriously, Jurassic World is the most amazing place in existence.

Between you and me, you have to be a little crazy to want to work at a place where your co-workers want to eat you. But, hey! If you stick with me and follow this book, you'll get to know and trust these amazing creatures in no time; not to mention, stay NOT eaten. Which is a very good thing.

Trust me, dinosaurs are way cooler than their distant relatives like lizards or crocodiles. They have way more scales and a lot more teeth! Awesome, right? Right. You haven't truly lived until you've sat on

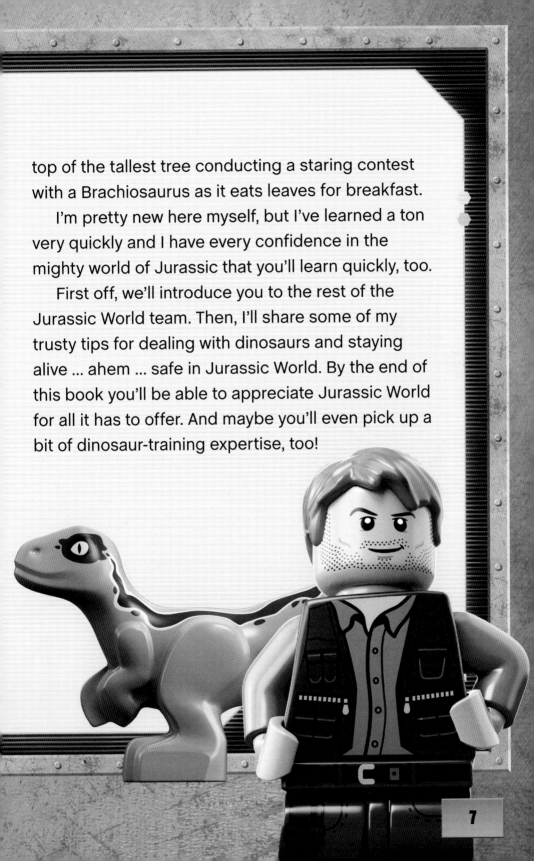

top of the tallest tree conducting a staring contest with a Brachiosaurus as it eats leaves for breakfast.

I'm pretty new here myself, but I've learned a ton very quickly and I have every confidence in the mighty world of Jurassic that you'll learn quickly, too.

First off, we'll introduce you to the rest of the Jurassic World team. Then, I'll share some of my trusty tips for dealing with dinosaurs and staying alive ... ahem ... safe in Jurassic World. By the end of this book you'll be able to appreciate Jurassic World for all it has to offer. And maybe you'll even pick up a bit of dinosaur-training expertise, too!

WHILE V
MEET LEC
OWEN

WHAT IS JURASSIC WORLD?

Jurassic World is a place of fun and family where fossils come alive! It's located on an island in the middle of nowhere and real-life dinosaurs live, play and eat here just like they did back in the Jurassic era! You're probably wondering how that's possible. Dinosaurs went extinct millions of years ago, right? Well, it turns out scientists found bits of dinosaur DNA trapped inside mosquitos, which were trapped inside pieces of amber and that amber was frozen inside ancient glaciers and by using the advanced science of genetic engineering...

Wow. That got complicated real fast. Here's all you really need to know. Dinosaurs live in Jurassic World exactly like they did millions of years ago, and now we humans can walk right alongside them! What could go wrong?

COME ON. THIS WILL BE FUN!

WALKING WITH DINOSAURS IS COOL!
(WHEN FOLLOWING THE PROPER SAFETY PROTOCOL)

Well, there was that one time it went wrong a bunch of years ago when the island was called Jurassic Park. The folks back then could have really used a safety video or maybe even a handy little guide like this one. A park employee didn't follow the rules, dinosaurs got loose and chased a bunch of people ... it was a bad day. But now Jurassic World does have a safety video, along with lots of safety equipment and warning signs. So it's totally safe!

STEEL GATES

LOTS OF SPACE

WARNING SIGNS

INDESTRUCTIBLE GYROSPHERES

WHO'S AT THE PARK!

Naturally, it takes a team of highly certified professionals to run Jurassic World. These folks help keep the park running and the dinosaur mayhem down to a bare minimum.

THIS IS CLAIRE.

She's the operations manager of Jurassic World and is always coming up with great ideas for new park attractions to keep visitors entertained. If you tell Claire she can't do something, there's a 99.9 per cent chance she'll make it happen. That leftover 0.1 per cent chance is for the times she's already made it happen.

SIMON MASRANI is the owner of the company that owns the company that owns Jurassic World. He loves cool dinosaurs almost as much as he loves flying helicopters and playing video games. (When he does both at the same time, he's gonna have a bad day.)

DR WU is the lead scientist for Jurassic World. His technology combines the features of different dinosaurs together into mega hybrid dinosaurs.

VIC HOSKINS is the head of park security. It's the perfect job for him because he loves tracking down and capturing escaped creatures. It's also the worst job for him because he's not really a team player.

OWEN GRADY

Owen is an animal behaviourist who discovers his ridiculously cool ability to bond with dinosaurs during his first trip to Jurassic World. Owen is always down for an adventure, especially with his best bud and dog companion, Red – which is why hanging around Jurassic World is the perfect fit! There always seems to be a problem afoot, and Owen is never one to shy away from an opportunity to help, especially if he can show off his building and fixing skills along the way.

EXCUSES ARE LIKE DINOSAURS: AN ENDANGERED SPECIES!

CLAIRE DEARING

Claire is the definition of a go-getter! She is strong, passionate and overflowing with new ideas to make Jurassic World the coolest place on the planet. She started at the park as the assistant operations manager and really impressed Simon, the owner of Jurassic World. Claire's the best at her job but also makes time to let loose and enjoy the fun times at the park.

SIMON MASRANI

Simon Masrani is the lucky owner of Jurassic World! Simple things like crustless sandwiches and dino-shaped cookies excite him. He is always thinking of the next BIG attraction for Jurassic World that will WOW the crowd times 100! How does he make these incredible, and sometimes ridiculous, ideas come to life? By making his team figure it all out for him, of course!

DR HENRY WU

Dr Wu runs the lab at Jurassic World. He is an amazing scientist who constantly pushes the boundaries of what it takes to build a real, live dinosaur! With Masrani challenging him to make bigger and better dinosaurs with each experiment, Dr Wu has a lot on his plate, but he loves every moment of his scientific research and is always eager for his next big breakthrough.

VIC HOSKINS

Vic is the head of security at Jurassic World, and boy, does he love it. Confident with a strong build, he has no problem zapping anything and everything that gets in his way. Fleeing *T. Rex*? Zap it! Wild herd of charging Gallimuses? Zap 'em! Kid acting up on the flume ride? Yeah, zap him too! His forceful tactics with the dinosaurs often get him into trouble, though, because he can't seem to understand one simple fact: if you respect them, maybe, just maybe, they'll respect you back.

DANNY NEDERMEYER

Danny is a handyman at Jurassic World! He does everything from fixing copiers to cleaning up messes, all with a smile! He really is a big help ... or at least that's what he wants everyone to think. Secretly, Danny is hungry for revenge and wants to destroy the park! The ultimate master of disguise, Danny uses his job to pull pranks around the park without anyone suspecting him.

ALLISON MILES

Allison is a top-notch scientist on Dr Wu's research team in the Jurassic World lab. She is full of ideas that often give Dr Wu the inspiration he needs to meet Masrani's insane dinosaur demands. She's willing to try anything in the name of science, even if it means baking the tastiest, most scientifically accurate cookies ever.

RED

Red is Owen's trusty sidekick and best friend. He may be a dog, but he has been by Owen's side through everything. Red loves adventure just as much as Owen, often saving Owen from some of his most outlandish ideas. He's one good boy!

BABY RAPTORS

Delta, Echo, Charlie and their leader, Blue, are baby raptors that have just arrived in Jurassic World, thanks to Owen delivering their eggs safely. They are highly intelligent and extremely prone to getting into trouble! These young dinosaurs may look cute, but make no mistake: they are ferocious.

Welcome to the most ferocious team ever! It's time to get down to dino business, so tell us a little about yourself. First, draw a picture of yourself on your very own Jurassic World Badge!

JURASSIC WORLD
ISLA NUBLAR

THE POWER OF TEAMWORK

The most important lesson I can teach you if you're gonna – I'm just going to come out and say it – survive Jurassic World. You need to work together with your friends and maybe even a few dinosaurs, in order to save the day. As I always like to say, there is no "i" in team. But there is an "i" in "dinosaur lunch".

Facing off against dinosaurs with your entire backup team: **BETTER IDEA**!

TEAMWORK FOR THE WIN!

Facing off against dinosaurs four-on-one: **BAD IDEA**.

TRUST YOUR TEAM

When you work together, you have to trust your team. If you only believe in yourself, how can you expect your team to have your back? You have to show them that you believe in them, too, in order for teamwork to be a success.

And for as much as you trust your team, you have to show them that you're trustworthy, too. How else do you think I'm able to get my Raptors to work together with me on rescue missions? It's all possible through trust.

TEAMWORK AND TRUST: ALWAYS A WINNING COMBINATION!

LET'S GET THIS DINOSAUR PARTY STARTED

So now that you know a little bit about the park and the people who work there, let's head on in through those fifty-foot-tall, double-thick steel gates and get down with some dinosaurs! Just remember to stick close or there's a good chance you could end up a dinosaur's lunch. I'm kidding! Kind of.

OWEN'S GUIDE TO TRAINING DINOSAURS

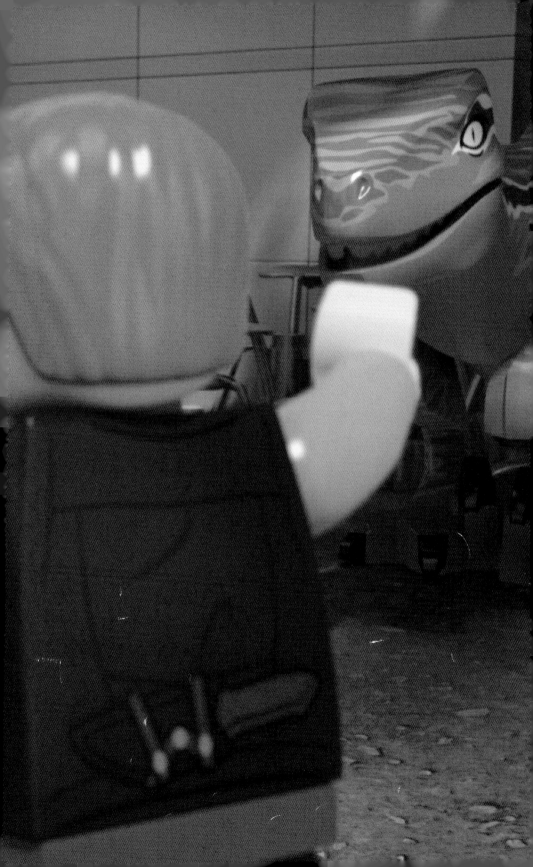

KNOWING YOUR DINOSAURS

LESSON #1 ABOUT JURASSIC WORLD: Dinosaurs are dangerous creatures. They are NOT pets. But you can have a fun time hanging out with them if you know which dinosaurs are friendly and which aren't. For example, some dinosaurs are herbivores, which means they only eat plants. They're cool to take a selfie with. Other dinosaurs are carnivores, meaning they only eat meat. What does that mean? It means put the selfie stick down and move far, far away.

If a dinosaur is snarling and growling and spitting goop, there's a good chance it's not selfie material.

Here's a handy checklist to help you remember which dinosaurs are herbivores (friendly!) and carnivores (less friendly!).

DINOSAURS THAT WILL EAT LUNCH WITH YOU:

BRACHIOSAURUS: Eats leaves for lunch.

TRICERATOPS: Eats bushes for lunch.

STEGOSAURUS: Eats salad for lunch. (It's on a diet.)

MAN IN DINOSAUR COSTUME: Not actually a dinosaur. But probably calling someone to see if they want to have lunch.

DINOSAURS THAT WILL EAT YOU FOR LUNCH

DILOPHOSAURUS: Spits gross goop at things that move and then eats them for lunch.

T. REX: Eats anything that moves for lunch.

VELOCIRAPTOR (YOU CAN JUST CALL THEM "RAPTORS"):

These guys are scary, sure, but they're also my buddies. Training Raptors is my specialty, and they're very smart.

TRAINING TACTICS

I SAW THAT, BLUE!
YOU BLINKED!

Part of being the alpha is staying calm at all times and showing the dinosaurs that I'm in control. Like when I'm going through my morning routine in the Raptor pen. I'm in charge of when it's breakfast time, nap time and playtime. Blue, Charlie and me are having a staring contest right here. Am I sweating right now? Only I know for sure.

The most important element of dinosaur training is trust. Remember how I told you dinosaurs aren't pets? They're not. So when it comes to training, I can never force a dinosaur to do something. (Actually, forcing them to do anything would pretty much guarantee a bad day.)

You and your dinosaur have to trust each other in order for the training to be a success. Even if you show them that you're the alpha, the only way to get a dinosaur to follow your commands is to earn their trust.

TRUSTY TIPS FOR DEALING WITH DINOSAURS

I hope you've been paying attention so far, but if you haven't then here are my top five trusty tips.

TRUSTY TIP #1: REMEMBER: DINOSAURS ARE *NOT* PETS!

TRUSTY TIP #2: NEVER TURN YOUR BACK TO THE CAGE.

TRUSTY TIP #3: RUNNING IS A LAST RESORT.

TRUSTY TIP #4: NEVER PLAY HIDE-AND-SEEK WITH A DINOSAUR.

TRUSTY TIP #5: TRUST ME. I'M A PROFESSIONAL.

QUIZ: DO YOU HAVE WHAT IT TAKES TO BE A DINOSAUR TRAINER?

Okay, rookie. There's an opening and the position has YOUR name written all over it. Let's see if you've got the right stuff.

1) Do you like working with animals?

2) Are you calm, cool and collected?

3) When assigned group projects, do you always take the lead?

4) Can you name ten different dinosaur species and the eras in which they lived?

5) Do your friends, family and even random acquaintances refer to you as alpha?

6) Do you gravitate towards extreme sports, like jungle parkour and lion taming?

7) Do you own or can you borrow a super cool vest?

8) Do you have experience handling large reptiles that haven't walked the earth in several million years?

9) In case of an emergency, can you run SUPER fast or hide really well?

IF YOU ANSWERED YES TO 3 QUESTIONS OR LESS:
Sorry to break it to you, rookie, but you have some pretty intensive training to do before you can go out into the wilds of Jurassic World and train some dinosaurs. But hard work pays off.

IF YOU ANSWERED YES TO 5 QUESTIONS: All right, you're on the right path. Training dinosaurs may be a little pie in the sky for you. But how about applying for a position at your local zoo? Good place to start learning the ropes!

IF YOU ANSWERED YES TO 7 QUESTIONS: Now we're talking! You like dinosaurs AND have the gumption to train them. Raptors are still a little out of your league. But Claire is always looking for people to staff the Dinosaur Petting Zoo.

IF YOU ANSWERED YES TO 9 QUESTIONS: Wow. You ... you really answered yes to all nine questions? Huh. I'm impressed. Okay, rookie. You're in. See you outside the Raptor pen, 8:00 sharp.

OWEN'S GUIDE TO STAYING SAFE

JURASSIC WORLD DOS AND DON'TS

We'll cover the basics for how we workers at Jurassic World keep things A-OK. But I'll bet you're thinking, "Owen, I don't want to work at Jurassic World. I just want to hang out with cool dinosaurs!" Well, everything I'll teach you still applies. But as a normal visitor to Jurassic World, you'll need to keep a few extra things in mind in order to make the best of it. And that starts with some simple dos and don'ts.

49

DO: WATCH THE SAFETY VIDEO

Claire hired a film crew to produce a special safety video for all Jurassic World employees that visitors might find helpful. As it turns out, it's not half-bad! Take a look.

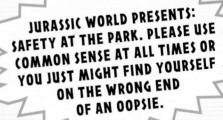

JURASSIC WORLD PRESENTS: SAFETY AT THE PARK. PLEASE USE COMMON SENSE AT ALL TIMES OR YOU JUST MIGHT FIND YOURSELF ON THE WRONG END OF AN OOPSIE.

DO: WATCH OUT FOR FAULTY PARK EQUIPMENT

You don't want to discover after the fact that the railing you were leaning against overlooking the Raptor pen was not securely in place.

DO: READ THE SAFETY SIGNS

Seriously, so many catastrophes could be avoided if people just read the signs. Follow these clearly posted instructions and you'll have a good day. Ignore them and it's bad-news Brachiosaurus.

DON'T: TRY TO CAPTURE THE DINOSAURS

Unless you're on a mission with all of park security to track down an escaped dinosaur, never ever go off on your own to capture a dinosaur. Don't be that guy. That guy always ends up having a bad day.

WOW. I GUESS YOU NEVER CAN UNDERRATE THE VALUE OF GOOD OLD COMMON SENSE.

KNOW YOUR WARNINGS

Here at Jurassic World, we use cautionary announcements to help Park guests know important information. Now, don't tell Claire I told you this – seriously, I could get in trouble – but the loudspeaker announcements are worded to keep everyone calm and not cause panic. The best way to appreciate Jurassic World is to know what each announcement actually means.

PARK CAUTIONARY ANNOUNCEMENTS

WHAT IT SAYS	WHAT IT MEANS
Valued patrons: Due to an unexpected shortage on hot dogs, all guests are encouraged to purchase alternate food choices.	The Indominus rex has eaten all the hot dogs ... and is still hungry.
Attention, guests: Due to technical difficulties, the Aviary is now closed.	The Aviary has been smashed and wild Pteranodons are now on the loose.
Dear visitors: Unanticipated but standard power surges may cause lights to flicker. Do not be alarmed.	A dinosaur has chewed through the main power grid and the park now has no power.
Please be advised: Due to a containment anomaly, all guests must seek shelter immediately.	THERE'S A MEGAMEAN DINOSAUR ON THE LOOSE!

QUIZ: DOS AND DON'TS

Pop quiz! Didn't think there'd be any of those in this book, huh? Well, there is! You just read a bunch of common-sense dos and don'ts about Jurassic World. Let's see if you were paying attention. Answer the following questions with yes or no.

1) You see a hot dog lying on the ground outside the Raptor cage. Ooh! It looks clean. Should you eat it?

2) You see footprints leaving the Indominus rex's compound. Huh, she must have left. You probably have time for a quick look around her nest, right?

3) You stumble into Dr Wu's lab. No one is around. All his technology looks so cool. Should you press a few buttons and see what happens?

4) Ooh! There's a hot dog costume in the lost property at Jurassic World. What better way to make a few bucks than to sell hot dogs dressed as a hot dog? Why not put it on and sell these snacks outside the Indominus rex's compound?

5) All the gyrospheres have been ordered back to base due to a "containment anomaly". But you're sure it's nothing serious. It's time for some off-roading, right?

6) That cute hybrid dinosaur just purred at you. At least it sounded like a purr. Could have been a snarl. You're not sure. But it was adorable. Want to pet it?

Answers #1–5: No!

Answer #6: No. If you answered yes, congratulations. You just became dinosaur lunch.

OWEN'S JURASSIC WORLD ESSENTIALS

At Jurassic World, you can only do your job if you have the proper equipment. Would you play a team sport without a uniform? No! Would you go into space without a spaceship? Of course not. Would you climb a cliff without a rope? Well, maybe. But the jungle is a dangerous place, especially when it's full of dinosaurs. Why am I telling you this? Well, if you're going to tango with dinosaurs, you need the right kit.

OWEN'S AWESOME OUTFIT:

SCRUFFY APPEARANCE
So it doesn't look like you care too much. Dinosaurs like to work for attention.

COTTON SHIRT
Nothing breathes like cotton.

UTILITY WAISTCOAT
Hidden compartments for snacks.

KNIFE
This is really just for chopping veggies. A balanced diet is very important.

DURABLE TROUSERS
If you thought grass stains were hard to get out, try getting out a dinosaur doo-doo stain.

OWEN'S COOL RIDES

GYROSPHERES: The best way for you to appreciate Jurassic World is from inside the scientifically enhanced glass orb of a gyrosphere.

MOTORCYCLES: Now, as for me, I prefer my trusty old hog (as in motorcycle). This bad boy gets me where I need to go every time. You need some pretty slick driving moves to escape an angry dinosaur on one of these things. But when you're a trainer like me, slick moves come with the territory.

MOBILE RESEARCH MODULE: For the rest of the Jurassic World crew, research modules are their go-to modes of transportation. These vehicles have reinforced metal walls and forty feet of cable used to lasso dinosaurs. That comes in handy when you have to track down a renegade dinosaur. In the jungle. At night.

–Reinforced titanium walls
–Monster-truck tyres
–Forty feet of tow cable

IT MAY BE PITCH-BLACK OUT HERE, BUT I FEEL SUPER SAFE!

–Steel roll cages
–Spare tyre
–LED headlights

4X4: And when all else fails, jump into a trusty 4x4 to make a getaway. You're always better off riding inside a vehicle than running on foot from a dinosaur. I really can't emphasize this enough: You cannot outrun a dinosaur.

DINOSAUR-WRANGLING GADGETS

Sometimes in Jurassic World, accidents happen. Dinosaurs escape. Bad things follow. The best thing to do in these situations is seek shelter and leave first response to the professionals. We're highly trained in the art of dinosaur wrangling and have a trusty assortment of gadgets at our command.

THWACK!

NETS: Not just for hair anymore.

LASSOS AND SLEEPY-TIME DARTS: For when you need to round up a whole herd of escaped dinosaurs. (That really shouldn't be happening, but it does more often than you'd think. We should probably look into that.)

THE TICKLER:
For when you need a dinosaur to spit something out. Like a large tree branch. Or a coworker.

QUIZ: THINK FAST!

You'll have to think fast to ace this quiz. Answer the questions below to see if your fast-thinking skills are up to speed or if they're as slow as a Raptor with a cold. (Ha! I crack myself up.)

1) When you get caught in an unexpected rainstorm, can you usually whip up an impromptu umbrella?

2) At the movies, do you note all the exits, keeping in mind that the nearest exit may be behind you?

3) When you're playing a team sport, are you able to use your opponent's weaknesses to your team's advantage?

4) If your normal route home from school is blocked, do you know every backup route and at least one shortcut?

5) Do you carry a torch with you at all times in the event of a power outage?

6) At a theme park, do you pay close attention to loudspeaker announcements?

7) If you were being chased by a dinosaur, would you run?*

QUIZ RESULTS: If you answered yes to every question except #7, congratulations! Your quick-thinking skills are top-notch.

*Ha! Trick question. Always ride away on a motorcycle. Never run.

OWEN
TO THE RESCUE

ADAPTED BY MEREDITH RUSU

FROM THE SCREENPLAY BY JEREMY ADAMS. STORY BY DAVID SHAYNE.

Welcome to Jurassic World, a theme park
with the most powerful dinosaurs ever!
Jurassic World sits on a big island.

Simon Masrani is the excitable owner of Jurassic World.

"We're going to open a new exhibit tonight!" he tells everyone. "A *secret* exhibit with three new dinosaurs!"

Masrani puts the smart Claire Dearing in charge of getting the three new dinosaurs to the island on time.

She has a cool animal trainer helping her. His name is Owen Grady.

Owen brings the three dinosaurs for the secret exhibit to Jurassic World on a helicopter. He also brings four Raptor eggs.

"Keep an eye on those eggs, Red," Owen tells his pet dog. "They're precious cargo."

When Owen arrives on the island, the
Raptor eggs hatch. One of the Raptors lets
Owen pet her!

"Would you look at that!" Owen smiles.
"They decided to come out and join the fun!"

Vic Hoskins is the head of security at Jurassic World. "You have a way with those dinosaurs," Vic tells Owen. "Ever thought about working here?"

"Nah," says Owen. "I'm just here to deliver the dinosaurs. Then I'm off!"

That's when Claire tells Owen his job isn't finished.

"You were supposed to deliver the dinosaurs to the *other* side of the island," she says. "So, if you want to get paid, you'll have to get a move on."

Owen starts to follow Claire. But suddenly, he spots a little boy playing in one of the park's Gyrospheres – clear, rolling balls that let visitors see the dinosaurs up close.

"Uh, I don't think you should do that!" Owen shouts.

But the kid doesn't listen. He speeds off!

No one sees the boy race away other than Owen.

That means Owen is the only one who can save the kid before he becomes a dinosaur's lunch! Yikes!

"Come on, Red!" Owen calls to his dog. "If I can get close, I can pull in front and slow the Gyrosphere down!"

Owen and Red stop the Gyrosphere just before it rolls off a cliff. The little boy is safe! But Owen is in trouble. A T. Rex has already spotted him!

"Sorry, Miss T. Rex, but I don't feel much like getting eaten right now," Owen says nervously.

Just when the T. Rex is about to chomp,
one of the baby Raptors sees that Owen is
in danger. She pulls Owen up to safety using
a vine.

"You just saved my life!" Owen says in
amazement. "Thank you!"

Little does Owen know, his troubles aren't over yet.

A worker named Danny Nedermeyer is up to no good. Danny really dislikes Simon Masrani and Jurassic World. And he plans to wreck the park – he wants it shut down for good!

When no one is looking, Danny uses a
computer to open the roof to the building where
all the flying dinosaurs live. A Pteranodon escapes
and swoops out into the park!

Vic is giving Owen a ride back to base in a helicopter when an alarm siren blares.

"Emergency!" a worker warns over the radio. "A Pteranodon has gotten loose!"

But it's too late. The Pteranodon smashes into the helicopter and stalls the engine.

"We need to kick-start the blades or we're going to crash!" Owen cries.

Thinking fast, he leaps from the helicopter, grabs on to the Pteranodon's legs and kicks the blades of the helicopter so they spin again.

Owen's plan works! The helicopter starts back up!

Vic is impressed. "You *really* have a way with those dinosaurs, kid!"

Safe and sound back at base, Owen
meets up with Claire.

"So, you finally decided to show back up
and finish your job?" she asks.

"Are you kidding?" Owen exclaims.
"Do you know what I just went through?!"

"I'm on a major time crunch," Claire insists. "If I don't get these three dinosaurs to their exhibit in time for the opening tonight, Simon will be furious!"

"Okay, here's the deal," Owen tells her. "I'll get you to the exhibit on time. But after that, I get paid."

Claire nods. "Deal."

Owen studies the map. "I think I see a shortcut that could save us some time," he says.

He steers them off the main road ... and accidently crashes into a T. Rex pen!

"That was close!" Claire exclaims. "But it's okay. As long as the light on the pen stays green, we're safe. The T. Rex can't escape."

Unfortunately, Danny is still up to his mischief. With a few taps on the keyboard, he unlocks the T. Rex pen and releases the dinosaur!

"AHHHHHHH!" scream Owen and Claire.

The T. Rex flips their truck over! The three dinosaurs for the exhibit escape, but Claire and Owen are trapped. They're in REAL trouble now!

"We have to get out of here!" Claire cries.

"I have an idea!" Owen tells her. He uses the broken pieces of the truck to build a getaway car. "Hold on tight!" he yells.

"There's only one way to deal with a grumpy dino," says Owen. "And that's a time-out!"

Owen aims a net cannon on the back of the getaway car at the T. Rex and fires!

Bull's-eye! Owen's shot is a direct hit. The T. Rex gets tangled in the net.

"Where do you want her?" Owen cheerfully asks Claire.

Claire shakes her head. "That was unbelievable. Are you *sure* you don't want to work here? You really have a way with dinos!"

Up in the control room, Danny is spotted by Masrani.

"What are you doing?" Masrani demands.

"Uh, nothing," Danny fibs. "Just ... fixing your copier."

Masrani stares for a long moment. "Oh, good!" he says. "It's been broken for weeks!"

While Masrani is distracted, Danny slips away. He'll continue his mischief another day.

Later that night, Owen and Claire watch with the crowd as Masrani unveils the park's secret exhibit.

"I give you the Dino Carousel!" Masrani announces.

"THAT'S the secret exhibit?" Owen asks in disbelief. "I almost became a T. Rex's dinner twice for a Dino Carousel?!"

Claire shrugs. "Masrani did say it was a surprise ... Well, weren't you surprised?"

"Yeah," Owen says. "A little TOO surprised!"

The next day, Owen has a surprise of his own for Claire and Vic.

"I've decided to work here at Jurassic World after all," he tells them. "Training these rascals has kind of grown on me. And after yesterday's adventure, how much crazier could anything get?"